HUMAN TARGET

"THE WANTED: EXTREMELY DEAD CONTRACT!"

Len Wein Writer **Bruno Redondo** Penciller **Sergio Sandoval** Inker
Jonny Rench Colorist **Wes Abbott** Letterer

"SCARS"

Peter Johnson (Chapters 1-2) * **Robbie Thompson** (Chapters 3-6) Writers
Chris Sprouse & Karl Story (Chapters 1, 3 & 5) **Simon Coleby & Cliff Rathburn** (Chapter 2)
Jason Masters (Chapter 4) **John Paul Leon** (Chapter 6)
Bruno Redondo & Sergio Sandoval (Chapter Opening Pages) Artists

* Special thanks to Matt Cherniss
Lee Bermejo Collection Cover Artist
The Human Target created by Len Wein & Carmine Infantino

Ben Abernathy	Editor-original series
Kristy Quinn	Assistant Editor
Bob Harras	Group Editor-Collected Editions
Anton Kawasaki	Editor
Robbin Brosterman	Design Director-Books
Louis Prandi	Art Director

DC COMICS

Diane Nelson	President
Dan DiDio and Jim Lee	Co-Publishers
Geoff Johns	Chief Creative Officer
Patrick Caldon	EVP-Finance and Admisitration
John Rood	EVP-Sales, Marketing and Business Development
Amy Genkins	SVP-Business and Legal Affairs
Steve Rotterdam	SVP-Sales and Marketing
John Cunningham	VP-Marketing
Terri Cunningham	VP-Managing Editor
Alison Gill	VP-Manufacturing
David Hyde	VP-Publicity
Sue Pohja	VP-Book Trade Sales
Alysse Soll	VP-Advertising and Custom Publishing
Bob Wayne	VP-Sales
Mark Chiarello	Art Director

HUMAN TARGET
Published by DC Comics. Cover, text and compilation Copyright © 2010 DC Comics. All Rights Reserved.

Originally published in single magazine form in HUMAN TARGET #1-6. Copyright © 2010 DC Comics. All Rights Reserved. All characters, their distinctive likenesses and related elements featured in this publication are trademarks of DC Comics. The stories, characters and incidents featured in this publication are entirely fictional. DC Comics does not read or accept unsolicited submissions of ideas, stories or artwork.

DC Comics, 1700 Broadway, New York, NY 10019
A Warner Bros. Entertainment Company
Printed by Printed by Quad/Graphics, Dubuque, IA, USA. 3/10/10. First printing.
ISBN 978-1-4012-2837-8

VENICE, THE HOTEL MARCHINI, SIX HOURS EARLIER...

OKAY, JUST KEEP YOUR HEADS *LOW* AND YOUR MOUTHS *SHUT*.

MY PEOPLE BOOKED THESE ROOMS FOR US UNDER THE NAME *GIORDANO*--

--AND THE SOONER WE'RE *INSIDE* AND OUT OF THE LINE OF FIRE, THE *HAPPIER* I'LL BE.

SO? HAPPY *NOW*, SIGNOR CHANCE?

COMPARATIVELY, ANGELICA.

JUST KEEP AWAY FROM THE *WINDOWS*, DON'T OPEN THE DOOR FOR ANYONE, AND WE'LL BE *FINE*.

YOU ARE A *DILIGENT* MAN, SIGNOR CHANCE.

I'M *PAID* TO BE.

GIVEN MY *DRUTHERS*, MORELLI, I'D HAPPILY THROW YOU TO THE *WOLVES* AND SELL TICKETS TO *WATCH*.

AND YOU ARE *HONEST*. ALSO AN ADMIRABLE TRAIT.

REMEMBER, EVERYTHING WE DO HERE IS AN ATTEMPT TO MAKE *AMENDS* FOR ALL OF MY PREVIOUS *SINS*.

TOO LITTLE, TOO LATE, FOR *MY* DIME--

--BUT I'LL STILL MAKE SURE YOU GET TO WASHINGTON *ALIVE*.

NOW, BOTH OF YOU, STAY PUT. I'VE GOT TO MAKE A *CALL*.

CHATEAU MARCEL, GENEVA, SWITZERLAND, SIX HOURS EARLIER!

I HOPE WE'RE ALMOST *DONE* WITH THIS COOKED GOOSE CHASE OF YOURS.

YOU HAVE NO IDEA THE *HOOPS* MY PEOPLE HAD TO JUMP THROUGH TO *ARRANGE* THESE LODGINGS FOR US.

THAT IS WHY YOU WERE *HIRED*, SIGNOR CHANCE.

DON'T *REMIND* ME.

MIGHT I ASSIST YOU WITH YOUR *MOTHER*, MONSIEUR?

NO THANKS. GOT IT *HANDLED*.

VERY WELL THEN.

LOCK THE *DOOR*.

I ALREADY *HAVE*. IT'S QUICKLY BECOMING A *HABIT*.

THERE ARE *WORSE* ONES TO HAVE.

I HAVE SUFFERED MANY *INDIGNITIES* IN THIS LIFE, SIGNOR CHANCE--

--BUT THIS IS BY FAR THE *WORST*.

HEY, AT LEAST I DIDN'T ASK YOU TO *SHAVE YOUR LEGS*.

SO, IT WENT *WELL?*

DEPENDS ON HOW YOU *LOOK* AT IT.

PLEASE, SIGNOR CHANCE, I'M TOO OLD FOR YOU TO PLAY *COY* WITH ME.

FINE THEN. IT'S AS SIMPLE AS *THIS...*

ON THE *ONE* HAND, I COLLECTED YOUR PRECIOUS *LEDGERS.*

ON THE *OTHER* HAND...

...THERE ARE FOUR MORE *BODIES* SPRAWLED ALL OVER THE MOUNTAINSIDE.

MORELLI, IT'S *ME*. OPEN THE *DOOR*.

AH, IT *IS* YOU, SIGNOR CHANCE.

YOU SHOULD BE MORE *CAREFUL*. I ALMOST *SHOT* YOU.

SO WHY SHOULD *YOU* BE ANY *DIFFERENT* THAN EVERYONE *ELSE* IN HONG KONG?

YOU *MEAN...?*

UNFORTUNATELY, *YES*. THE BODY COUNT KEEPS *CLIMBING*.

IN THE MEANTIME, HERE ARE YOUR *LEDGERS*.

TELL ME WE'RE FINALLY *DONE* WITH THIS.

WE *ARE*. OUR NEXT STOP IS *WASHINGTON*.

PAPA, PLEASE--I *BEG* YOU--DO NOT *DO* THIS TERRIBLE THING.

YOU WILL *BETRAY* EVERYTHING YOU ONCE SWORE TO LOVE AND *DEFEND*.

STILL YOU DO NOT *UNDERSTAND*, ANGELICA? I DO THIS ALL FOR *YOU!*

I AM A DYING OLD MAN. A *CLEAN SLATE*--A NEW *LEASE* ON LIFE--IS ALL I HAVE OF WORTH TO *LEAVE* YOU.

BUT YOU SWORE A *BLOOD OATH* TO BE TRUE TO THE *FAMILY*--!

YOU ARE MY FAMILY, DAUGHTER--AND *ONLY* YOU!

THE END...
FOR NOW

SAN FRANCISCO.
TWO YEARS AGO.

HMM.

THIS ISN'T GOOD.

DOUBT HE'S HERE FOR MY VINYL COLLECTION. OR THE VINTAGE SPORTS ILLUSTRATED'S PILING UP IN THE CLOSET.

HE'S ALSO NOT ALONE. LET'S COUNT THEM OFF, SHALL WE?

ONE DOWN.

HE'S UGLY AND HE'S MEAN AND HE SMELLS LIKE CHINESE TAKE-OUT.

WHAM

AAAGH!

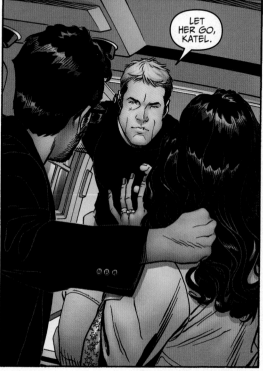

LET HER GO, KATEL.

WITH PLEASURE.

HOLD ON!

I--I CAN'T GET A GRIP. YOUR BLOOD--

HOLD ON, LET ME--

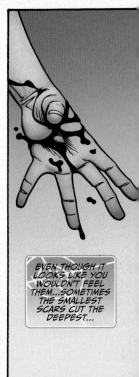

EVEN THOUGH IT LOOKS LIKE YOU WOULDN'T FEEL THEM...SOMETIMES THE SMALLEST SCARS CUT THE DEEPEST...

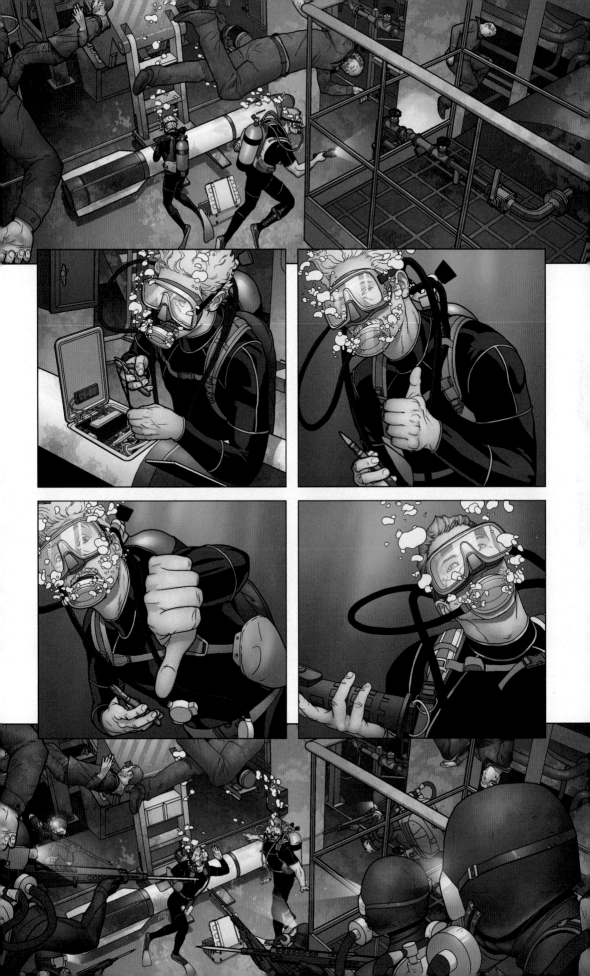

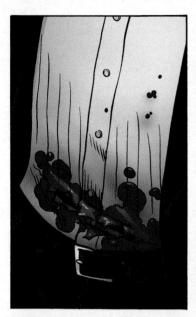

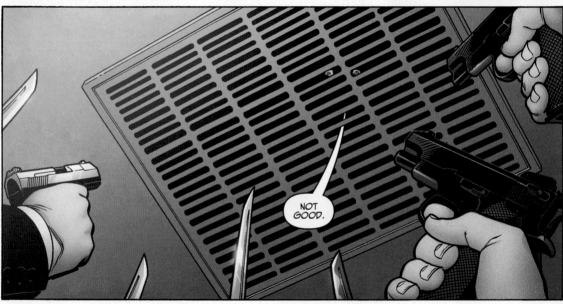

NOT GOOD.

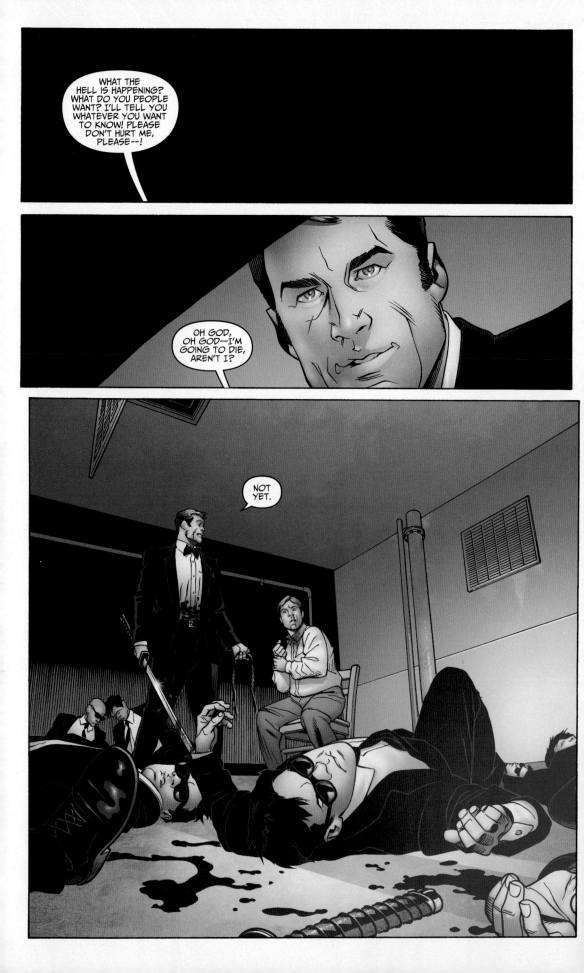

MY WORK ISN'T JUST ALL ABOUT PUNCHING, THOUGH. SOMETIMES IT'S ABOUT KICKING.

MOST OF THE TIME IT'S ABOUT FINDING THE LITTLE DETAILS OF THE CASE.

SEEING HOW THEY ALL ADD UP.

IT LOOKS SOMETHING LIKE THIS...

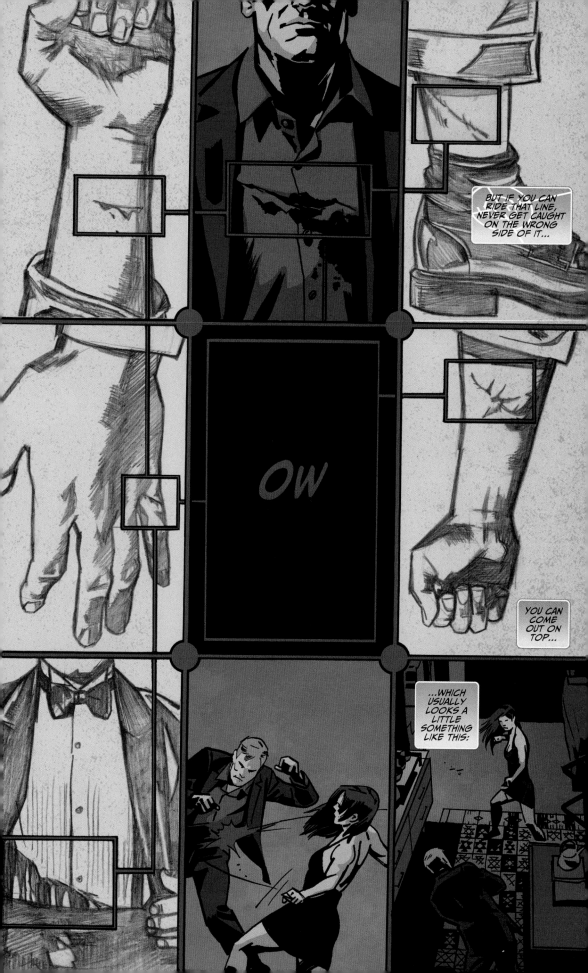

COVER GALLERY

Human Target #1
Cover art by Lee Bermejo